Random House   New York

The Alphabet Tale

by Jan Garten / Illustrated by Muriel Batherman

Sharp eyes and sharp teeth—

Run first and look later—

This tail is the tail of the _ _ _ _ _ _ _ _

Alligator

In building dams he's a great believer.

This tail is the tail of the busy_____

Beaver

Softly he walks, pitter pat.

This tail is the tail of the meowing___

Cat

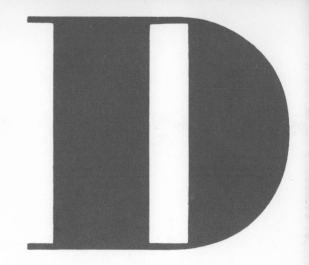

You pin it on him at parties

When you can't see.

This tail is the tail of the long-eared _____

Donkey

A gray nose long, a gray tail scant,

This tail is the tail of the_____

Elephant

A prowler sly is frightening the flocks.

This tail is the tail of the red-haired___

Fox

A neck so long it makes you laugh.

This tail is the tail of the tall_____

Giraffe

You gallop him on prairies

And on carousels, of course.

This tail is the tail of the prancing_____

Horse

He's measuring, measuring, squirm by squirm.

This tail is the tail of the wriggly_____

Inchworm

He roams the forest both near and far.

This tail is the tail of the spotted_____

Jaguar

Watch him hopping in the zoo.

This tail is the tail of the _____

Kangaroo

The king of the beasts

                Is a ruler all shun.

This tail is the tail of the roaring____

Lion

M

Someone high in the branches
Is chattering with glee.
This tail is the tail of the gay_____

Monkey

N

He silently swims his watery route.

This tail is the tail of the slippery ____

Newt

Spreading out with a beautiful swish,

This tail is the tail of the plumed_____

Ostrich

Better beware of each prickly spine.

This tail is the tail of the _____

Porcupine

He nests on the ground, his feathers are pale.
This tail is the tail of the plump little_____

Quail

R

His forefather was the hat
of Daniel Boone.
This tail is the tail of the furry_____

Raccoon

He balances balls and swims a great deal.

This tail is the tail of the flippered _ _ _ _

Seal

All are frightened by his growling Grrrr.

This tail is the tail of the fierce_____

Tiger

U

He lives in make-believe land
With his one long horn.
This tail is the the tail of the _____

Unicorn

V

Circling his prey as his wide wings whirr,
This tail is the tail of the greedy_____

Vulture

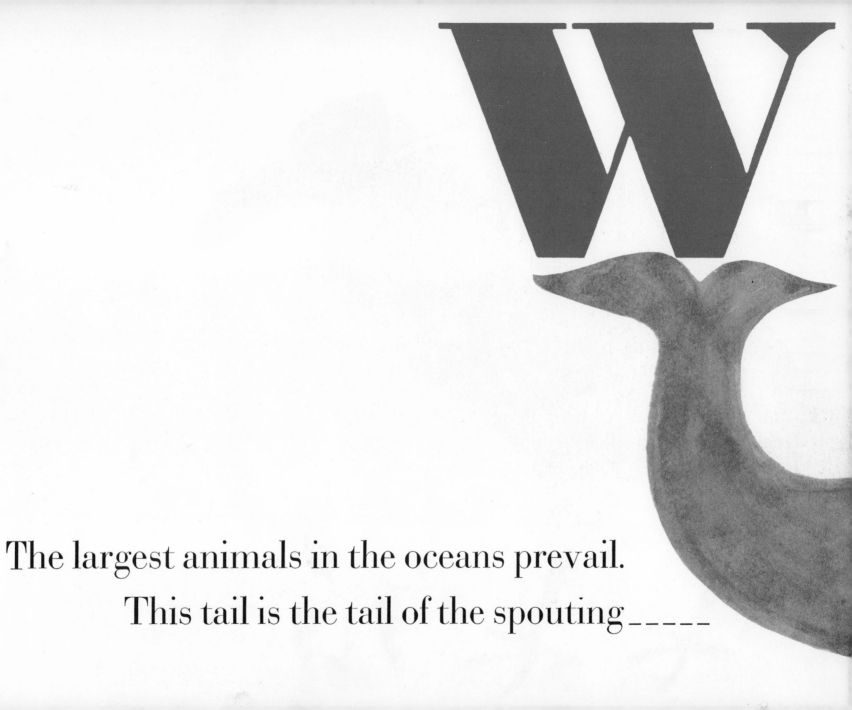

The largest animals in the oceans prevail.
This tail is the tail of the spouting_____

Whale

A strange beast lives far distant from us.

This tail is the tail of the_____

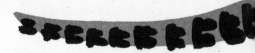

Xenurus

A long-haired cow eats grass for a snack.

This tail is the tail of the bushy ___

Yak

This striped tail is the last tail. Who will it be
to end the alphabet with a black and white Z?

Zebra